C000257911

Elvis

Story written by Gill Munton
Illustrated by Tim Archbold

Speed Sounds

Consonants   *Ask children to say the sounds.*

f	l	m	n	r	s	v	z	**sh**	**th**	**ng**
ff	**ll**		nn		**ss**	ve	zz			**nk**
							s			

b	c	d	g	h	j	p	qu	t	w	x	y	ch
bb	k		gg			pp		tt	wh			**tch**
	ck											

Each box contains one sound but sometimes more than one grapheme.
*Focus graphemes for this story are **circled**.*

4

Vowels

Ask children to say the sounds in and out of order.

a	e	i	o	u
at	hen	in	on	up

ay	ee	igh	ow	oo
day	see	high	blow	zoo

Story Green Words

Ask children to read the words first in Fred Talk and then say the word.

elf   tap   witch   wand   imp   stitch   king
cash   doll   dress

Ask children to say the syllables and then read the whole word.

El|vis

Ask children to read the root first and then the whole word with the suffix.

mend → mending   sock → socks

6

Red Words

Ask children to practise reading the words across the rows, down the columns and in and out of order clearly and quickly.

I	you	the
my	your	are
said	go	of
to	no	be

Elvis

Elvis is an elf.

His job is mending things.

Tap! Tap! Tap!

"I am Elvis the elf!"
Elvis sang.

"I can mend
the witch's wand ..."

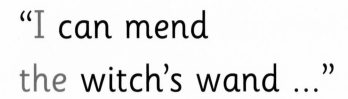

Tap tap

"I can mend
the imp's red hat ..."

Stitch stitch

"I can mend the king's big black cash box ..."

Tap tap

"I can mend the doll's pink dress ..."

Stitch stitch

"Can you mend my socks?"

Questions to talk about

Ask children to TTYP for each question using 'Fastest finger' (FF) or 'Have a think' (HaT).

p.8 (FF) What kind of creature is Elvis?

p.10 (FF) What does Elvis sing as he works?

p.11 (FF) What does the imp ask Elvis to mend?

p.12 (FF) What does the king ask Elvis to mend?

p.13 (Hat) What do you think Elvis thinks when the giant asks him to mend his socks?